AF753078

2201 $

DATE 20

TO

FOR

	Dollars	Cents
Balance Forward		
Deposited		
Deposited		
TOTAL		
This Check		
Balance		

Fit & Fashionable

800 Coco Drive, Coconut Grove, FL 33133

2201

20

Pay to the Order of $

Dollars

(For Classroom Use Only)

South Miami Bank

For

⑆74 0020441⑆ 2⑈099 1⑈2201

2202 $

DATE 20

TO

FOR

	Dollars	Cents
Balance Forward		
Deposited		
Deposited		
TOTAL		
This Check		
Balance		

Fit & Fashionable

800 Coco Drive, Coconut Grove, FL 33133

2202

20

Pay to the Order of $

Dollars

(For Classroom Use Only)

South Miami Bank

For

⑆74 0020441⑆ 2⑈099 1⑈2202

2203 $

DATE 20

TO

FOR

	Dollars	Cents
Balance Forward		
Deposited		
Deposited		
TOTAL		
This Check		
Balance		

Fit & Fashionable

800 Coco Drive, Coconut Grove, FL 33133

2203

20

Pay to the Order of $

Dollars

(For Classroom Use Only)

South Miami Bank

For

⑆74 0020441⑆ 2⑈099 1⑈2203

2204 $

DATE 20

TO

FOR

	Dollars	Cents
Balance Forward		
Deposited		
Deposited		
TOTAL		
This Check		
Balance		

Fit & Fashionable

800 Coco Drive, Coconut Grove, FL 33133

2204

20

Pay to the Order of $

Dollars

(For Classroom Use Only)

South Miami Bank

For

⑆74 0020441⑆ 2⑈099 1⑈2204

2205

$ ____________

DATE ____________ 20 ____

TO ____________

FOR ____________

	Dollars	Cents
Balance Forward		
Deposited		
Deposited		
TOTAL		
This Check		
Balance		

Fit & Fashionable

800 Coco Drive, Coconut Grove, FL 33133

2205

____________ 20 ____

Pay to the Order of ____________ $ ____________

____________ Dollars

(For Classroom Use Only)

South Miami Bank

For ____________ ____________

⑆ 74 002044⑆ 2⑈099 1⑈2205

2206

$ ____________

DATE ____________ 20 ____

TO ____________

FOR ____________

	Dollars	Cents
Balance Forward		
Deposited		
Deposited		
TOTAL		
This Check		
Balance		

Fit & Fashionable

800 Coco Drive, Coconut Grove, FL 33133

2206

____________ 20 ____

Pay to the Order of ____________ $ ____________

____________ Dollars

(For Classroom Use Only)

South Miami Bank

For ____________ ____________

⑆ 74 002044⑆ 2⑈099 1⑈2206

2207

$ ____________

DATE ____________ 20 ____

TO ____________

FOR ____________

	Dollars	Cents
Balance Forward		
Deposited		
Deposited		
TOTAL		
This Check		
Balance		

Fit & Fashionable

800 Coco Drive, Coconut Grove, FL 33133

2207

____________ 20 ____

Pay to the Order of ____________ $ ____________

____________ Dollars

(For Classroom Use Only)

South Miami Bank

For ____________ ____________

⑆ 74 002044⑆ 2⑈099 1⑈2207

2208

$ ____________

DATE ____________ 20 ____

TO ____________

FOR ____________

	Dollars	Cents
Balance Forward		
Deposited		
Deposited		
TOTAL		
This Check		
Balance		

Fit & Fashionable

800 Coco Drive, Coconut Grove, FL 33133

2208

____________ 20 ____

Pay to the Order of ____________ $ ____________

____________ Dollars

(For Classroom Use Only)

South Miami Bank

For ____________ ____________

⑆ 74 002044⑆ 2⑈099 1⑈2208

2209 $ ____________

DATE ____________ 20 ____

TO ____________

FOR ____________

	Dollars	Cents
Balance Forward		
Deposited		
Deposited		
TOTAL		
This Check		
Balance		

Fit & Fashionable

800 Coco Drive, Coconut Grove, FL 33133

2209

____________ 20 ____

Pay to the Order of ____________________ $ ________

____________________ Dollars

(For Classroom Use Only)

South Miami Bank

For ____________ ____________

⑆ 74 002044⑆ 2⑈099 1⑈2209

2210 $ ____________

DATE ____________ 20 ____

TO ____________

FOR ____________

	Dollars	Cents
Balance Forward		
Deposited		
Deposited		
TOTAL		
This Check		
Balance		

Fit & Fashionable

800 Coco Drive, Coconut Grove, FL 33133

2210

____________ 20 ____

Pay to the Order of ____________________ $ ________

____________________ Dollars

(For Classroom Use Only)

South Miami Bank

For ____________ ____________

⑆ 74 002044⑆ 2⑈099 1⑈2210

2211 $ ____________

DATE ____________ 20 ____

TO ____________

FOR ____________

	Dollars	Cents
Balance Forward		
Deposited		
Deposited		
TOTAL		
This Check		
Balance		

Fit & Fashionable

800 Coco Drive, Coconut Grove, FL 33133

2211

____________ 20 ____

Pay to the Order of ____________________ $ ________

____________________ Dollars

(For Classroom Use Only)

South Miami Bank

For ____________ ____________

⑆ 74 002044⑆ 2⑈099 1⑈2211

2212 $ ____________

DATE ____________ 20 ____

TO ____________

FOR ____________

	Dollars	Cents
Balance Forward		
Deposited		
Deposited		
TOTAL		
This Check		
Balance		

Fit & Fashionable

800 Coco Drive, Coconut Grove, FL 33133

2212

____________ 20 ____

Pay to the Order of ____________________ $ ________

____________________ Dollars

(For Classroom Use Only)

South Miami Bank

For ____________ ____________

⑆ 74 002044⑆ 2⑈099 1⑈2212

2213 $ ____________

DATE	20	
TO		
FOR		
	Dollars	Cents
Balance Forward		
Deposited		
Deposited		
TOTAL		
This Check		
Balance		

Fit & Fashionable **2213**

800 Coco Drive, Coconut Grove, FL 33133 ____________ 20 ____

Pay to the Order of ______________________________ $ ____________

______________________________ Dollars

(For Classroom Use Only)

South Miami Bank

For ____________ ____________________

⑆ 74 0020441⑆ 2⑈099 1⑈2213

2214 $ ____________

DATE	20	
TO		
FOR		
	Dollars	Cents
Balance Forward		
Deposited		
Deposited		
TOTAL		
This Check		
Balance		

Fit & Fashionable **2214**

800 Coco Drive, Coconut Grove, FL 33133 ____________ 20 ____

Pay to the Order of ______________________________ $ ____________

______________________________ Dollars

(For Classroom Use Only)

South Miami Bank

For ____________ ____________________

⑆ 74 0020441⑆ 2⑈099 1⑈2214

2215 $ ____________

DATE	20	
TO		
FOR		
	Dollars	Cents
Balance Forward		
Deposited		
Deposited		
TOTAL		
This Check		
Balance		

Fit & Fashionable **2215**

800 Coco Drive, Coconut Grove, FL 33133 ____________ 20 ____

Pay to the Order of ______________________________ $ ____________

______________________________ Dollars

(For Classroom Use Only)

South Miami Bank

For ____________ ____________________

⑆ 74 0020441⑆ 2⑈099 1⑈2215

2216 $ ____________

DATE	20	
TO		
FOR		
	Dollars	Cents
Balance Forward		
Deposited		
Deposited		
TOTAL		
This Check		
Balance		

Fit & Fashionable **2216**

800 Coco Drive, Coconut Grove, FL 33133 ____________ 20 ____

Pay to the Order of ______________________________ $ ____________

______________________________ Dollars

(For Classroom Use Only)

South Miami Bank

For ____________ ____________________

⑆ 74 0020441⑆ 2⑈099 1⑈2216

2217 $

DATE 20		
TO		
FOR		
	Dollars	Cents
Balance Forward		
Deposited		
Deposited		
TOTAL		
This Check		
Balance		

Fit & Fashionable **2217**

800 Coco Drive, Coconut Grove, FL 33133 ______ 20 ____

Pay to the Order of ______ $ ______

______ Dollars

(For Classroom Use Only)

South Miami Bank

For ______

⑆ 74 0020441⑆ 2⑈099 1⑈2217

2218 $

DATE 20		
TO		
FOR		
	Dollars	Cents
Balance Forward		
Deposited		
Deposited		
TOTAL		
This Check		
Balance		

Fit & Fashionable **2218**

800 Coco Drive, Coconut Grove, FL 33133 ______ 20 ____

Pay to the Order of ______ $ ______

______ Dollars

(For Classroom Use Only)

South Miami Bank

For ______

⑆ 74 0020441⑆ 2⑈099 1⑈2218

2219 $

DATE 20		
TO		
FOR		
	Dollars	Cents
Balance Forward		
Deposited		
Deposited		
TOTAL		
This Check		
Balance		

Fit & Fashionable **2219**

800 Coco Drive, Coconut Grove, FL 33133 ______ 20 ____

Pay to the Order of ______ $ ______

______ Dollars

(For Classroom Use Only)

South Miami Bank

For ______

⑆ 74 0020441⑆ 2⑈099 1⑈2219

2220 $

DATE 20		
TO		
FOR		
	Dollars	Cents
Balance Forward		
Deposited		
Deposited		
TOTAL		
This Check		
Balance		

Fit & Fashionable **2220**

800 Coco Drive, Coconut Grove, FL 33133 ______ 20 ____

Pay to the Order of ______ $ ______

______ Dollars

(For Classroom Use Only)

South Miami Bank

For ______

⑆ 74 0020441⑆ 2⑈099 1⑈2220

No. ______ $ ______

DATE ______ 20 ______

TO ______

FOR ______

	Dollars	Cents
Balance Forward		
Deposited		
Deposited		
TOTAL		
This Check		
Balance		

Fit & Fashionable

800 Coco Drive, Coconut Grove, FL 33133

No. ______

______ 20 ______

Pay to the Order of ______ $______

______ Dollars

(For Classroom Use Only)

South Miami Bank

For ______ ______

⑆ 74 0020441⑆ 2⑈099 1⑈

No. ______ $ ______

DATE ______ 20 ______

TO ______

FOR ______

	Dollars	Cents
Balance Forward		
Deposited		
Deposited		
TOTAL		
This Check		
Balance		

Fit & Fashionable

800 Coco Drive, Coconut Grove, FL 33133

No. ______

______ 20 ______

Pay to the Order of ______ $______

______ Dollars

(For Classroom Use Only)

South Miami Bank

For ______ ______

⑆ 74 0020441⑆ 2⑈099 1⑈

No. ______ $ ______

DATE ______ 20 ______

TO ______

FOR ______

	Dollars	Cents
Balance Forward		
Deposited		
Deposited		
TOTAL		
This Check		
Balance		

Fit & Fashionable

800 Coco Drive, Coconut Grove, FL 33133

No. ______

______ 20 ______

Pay to the Order of ______ $______

______ Dollars

(For Classroom Use Only)

South Miami Bank

For ______ ______

⑆ 74 0020441⑆ 2⑈099 1⑈

No. ______ $ ______

DATE ______ 20 ______

TO ______

FOR ______

	Dollars	Cents
Balance Forward		
Deposited		
Deposited		
TOTAL		
This Check		
Balance		

Fit & Fashionable

800 Coco Drive, Coconut Grove, FL 33133

No. ______

______ 20 ______

Pay to the Order of ______ $______

______ Dollars

(For Classroom Use Only)

South Miami Bank

For ______ ______

⑆ 74 0020441⑆ 2⑈099 1⑈

No. ______ $ ______
DATE 20 ______
TO
FOR

	Dollars	Cents
Balance Forward		
Deposited		
Deposited		
TOTAL		
This Check		
Balance		

Fit & Fashionable

800 Coco Drive, Coconut Grove, FL 33133

No. ______

______ 20 ______

Pay to the Order of ______ $ ______

______ Dollars

(For Classroom Use Only)

South Miami Bank

For ______ ______

⑆ 74 0020441⑆ 2⑈099 1⑈

No. ______ $ ______
DATE 20 ______
TO
FOR

	Dollars	Cents
Balance Forward		
Deposited		
Deposited		
TOTAL		
This Check		
Balance		

Fit & Fashionable

800 Coco Drive, Coconut Grove, FL 33133

No. ______

______ 20 ______

Pay to the Order of ______ $ ______

______ Dollars

(For Classroom Use Only)

South Miami Bank

For ______ ______

⑆ 74 0020441⑆ 2⑈099 1⑈

No. ______ $ ______
DATE 20 ______
TO
FOR

	Dollars	Cents
Balance Forward		
Deposited		
Deposited		
TOTAL		
This Check		
Balance		

Fit & Fashionable

800 Coco Drive, Coconut Grove, FL 33133

No. ______

______ 20 ______

Pay to the Order of ______ $ ______

______ Dollars

(For Classroom Use Only)

South Miami Bank

For ______ ______

⑆ 74 0020441⑆ 2⑈099 1⑈

No. ______ $ ______
DATE 20 ______
TO
FOR

	Dollars	Cents
Balance Forward		
Deposited		
Deposited		
TOTAL		
This Check		
Balance		

Fit & Fashionable

800 Coco Drive, Coconut Grove, FL 33133

No. ______

______ 20 ______

Pay to the Order of ______ $ ______

______ Dollars

(For Classroom Use Only)

South Miami Bank

For ______ ______

⑆ 74 0020441⑆ 2⑈099 1⑈

No. ______	$ ____________
DATE	20
TO	
FOR	

	Dollars	Cents
Balance Forward		
Deposited		
Deposited		
TOTAL		
This Check		
Balance		

Fit & Fashionable

800 Coco Drive, Coconut Grove, FL 33133

No. ________

________________ 20 ____

Pay to the Order of ______________________________ $__________

____ Dollars

(For Classroom Use Only)

South Miami Bank

For ________________ ________________

⑆74 0020441⑆ 2⑈099 1⑈

No. ______	$ ____________
DATE	20
TO	
FOR	

	Dollars	Cents
Balance Forward		
Deposited		
Deposited		
TOTAL		
This Check		
Balance		

Fit & Fashionable

800 Coco Drive, Coconut Grove, FL 33133

No. ________

________________ 20 ____

Pay to the Order of ______________________________ $__________

____ Dollars

(For Classroom Use Only)

South Miami Bank

For ________________ ________________

⑆74 0020441⑆ 2⑈099 1⑈

No. ______	$ ____________
DATE	20
TO	
FOR	

	Dollars	Cents
Balance Forward		
Deposited		
Deposited		
TOTAL		
This Check		
Balance		

Fit & Fashionable

800 Coco Drive, Coconut Grove, FL 33133

No. ________

________________ 20 ____

Pay to the Order of ______________________________ $__________

____ Dollars

(For Classroom Use Only)

South Miami Bank

For ________________ ________________

⑆74 0020441⑆ 2⑈099 1⑈

No. ______	$ ____________
DATE	20
TO	
FOR	

	Dollars	Cents
Balance Forward		
Deposited		
Deposited		
TOTAL		
This Check		
Balance		

Fit & Fashionable

800 Coco Drive, Coconut Grove, FL 33133

No. ________

________________ 20 ____

Pay to the Order of ______________________________ $__________

____ Dollars

(For Classroom Use Only)

South Miami Bank

For ________________ ________________

⑆74 0020441⑆ 2⑈099 1⑈